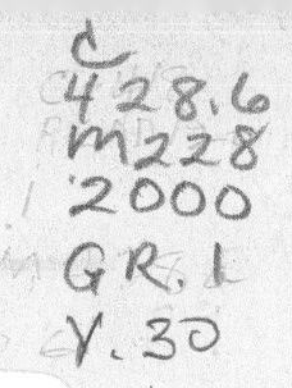

GRAMMAR
PRACTICE BOOK

Grade 1

Macmillan McGraw-Hill

New York • Farmington

CONTENTS

LEVEL 1

I Went Walking

Rain

Five Little Ducks

The Chick and the Duckling

The Good Bad Cat

My Friends

Level 2

Bet You Can't

Coco Can't Wait!

Down by the Bay

Jasper's Beanstalk

LEVEL 3

An Egg Is an Egg

Whose Baby?

Everything Grows

White Rabbit's Color Book

Hattie and the Fox

Any Kind of Dog

Seven Sillies

The Story of Chicken Licken

One Monday Morning

You'll Soon Grow into Them, Titch

Seven Blind Mice

The Surprise Family

In the Attic

Julieta and Her Paintbox

Jimmy Lee Did It

New Shoes for Silvia

Level 5, Unit 2

Just a Little Bit

A Birthday Basket for Tía

Guinea Pigs Don't Read Books

A Letter to Amy

SENTENCES

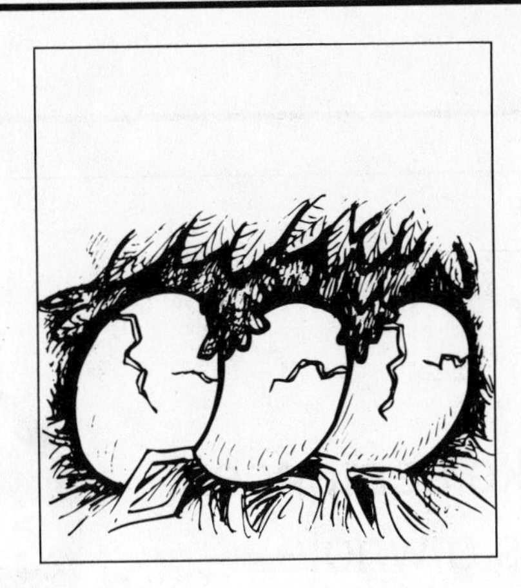

Look at the pictures.
They tell a story.
Then draw a circle around each correct sentence.

1. The duck is sitting on the eggs.

   The duck on three eggs.

2. Are cracking and hatching.

   The eggs are cracking.

3. Did ducks hatch from the eggs?

   Dinosaurs from the eggs?

4. Mother duck surprised?

   Is the mother duck surprised?

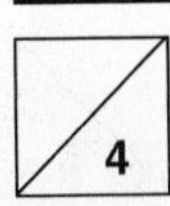

Extension: You may wish to have children use a complete sentence to tell what the mother duck might have said.

Name: Date:

SENTENCES TELL WHOLE THOUGHTS

Remember

- Words can make sentences.
- A sentence tells a whole thought.

The cat found a new friend.

Draw a circle around each correct sentence.

1. A cat said, "Meow."
2. Looked at us.
3. The duck saw the cat.
4. I see a lot of cats.
5. Went walking.

Extension: You may wish to have children say complete sentences about a real or imaginary cat.

Name: Date:

SENTENCES THAT TELL

Remember

- Some sentences tell something.

The three pigs are eating.

Make five sentences that tell something.
Draw a line from the words on the left to the words on the right.

1. That dog	are eating.
2. The pigs	tastes good.
3. The food	likes to eat bones.
4. I saw	likes to eat hay.
5. The horse	a black cat.

Extension: Have children say a sentence that includes the sound one of the animals makes. For example, "The cat says, 'Meow.'"

Name: ______________________ Date: ______________________

SENTENCES THAT ASK

Remember

- Some sentences ask something.
- Sentences that ask something are questions.

Do you think it will rain?

Draw a circle around each question.

1. Can a duck talk?

2. A horse is bigger than a duck.

3. What color is a duck?

4. A duck says, "Quack."

5. Is a duck as big as a horse?

Extension: You may wish to have children take turns asking partners questions and answering the questions.

Name: ______________________ Date: ______________

A LETTER TO UNCLE JACK

Write a letter to Uncle Jack.
Write one sentence that tells something about the picture.
Write one sentence that asks a question.

Dear Uncle Jack,

____

____

____

____

Love,

____

Extension: You may wish to invite children to write more sentences for the letter.

Name: Date:

SENTENCES

Read the poems.
One poem has three complete sentences.
Draw a circle around that poem.

A. Rain, rain, go away.

Come again another day.

Little Johnny wants to play.

B. Rain on the green grass

And rain on the tree,

Rain on the house-top

But not on me.

Extension: You may wish to have children recite each poem, using gestures.

Name: ______________________ Date: ______________

COMPLETING SENTENCES

Remember

A sentence tells a whole thought. Jed likes the rain.

Find the words that tell something about the picture.
Write the words to complete each sentence.

looks outside	fall	reads a book	eats a bone

1. A boy ______________________.

2. The girl ______________________.

3. The dog ______________________.

4. Raindrops ______________________.

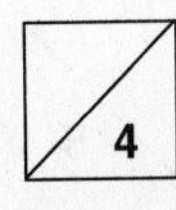

Extension: You may wish to have children make up sentences about how they feel on rainy days.

WORDS THAT ARE NOT SENTENCES

Remember

Sometimes a group of words does not tell a whole thought.

Words that do not tell a whole thought do not make a sentence.

A storm

This is not a sentence.

Which words do not tell a whole thought? Draw a circle around them.

1. Storms
2. Pours down
3. Rain helps farmers.
4. Windy
5. Gray sky

Extension: You may wish to have children complete one or more of the incomplete sentences.

SENTENCES AND NOT SENTENCES

Remember

A sentence must tell a whole thought.

We see three cars.
sentence

Three cars
not a sentence

Which words tell a whole thought?
Draw a circle around the sentences.

1. The black car

2. The black car is very big.

3. The next car is red.

4. Next car

5. One car has no top.

6. Has no top

Extension: You may wish to have children supply the missing parts for the incomplete sentences.

Name: Date:

COMPLETING SENTENCES

Color in the picture.

The sentences tell you how.

1. The tall flowers are yellow.

2. The woman wears a blue hat.

3. The small flowers are red.

4. The garden hose is green.

5. Purple flowers grow on bushes.

Extension: You may wish to have children draw a garden and write their own sentences about their pictures.

Name: Date:

STARTING AND ENDING SENTENCES

Draw a circle around the sentences that ask something.

1. Where is the mother?

2. Five ducks swim.

3. Who is first?

4. Where is the baby?

5. I like ducks.

6. Find the mother.

7. Who can swim?

8. I can swim.

8

Extension: Have children answer the questions.

BEGINNING AND ENDING SENTENCES

Remember

A sentence tells a whole thought.
A sentence begins with a capital letter.
A sentence ends with a special mark.
The mark is a period or a question mark.

A duck quacks **.** **D** oes a cow quack **?**

Draw a circle around the letter that should be a capital letter.

1. the bird sang a sweet song.
2. can a duck quack?
3. what does a rooster sing?

Draw a circle around the end mark in each sentence.

4. Why did the mouse squeak?
5. "Moo," said the cow.

Extension: Have children make up other statements and questions about animals.

Name: ______________________ Date: ______________________

ENDING WITH A PERIOD

Remember

A sentence that tells a whole thought is a statement.
A statement ends with a period.

Trees grow on that hill __.__

Read each sentence. Draw a circle around the period.

1. Flowers grow there.

2. Some birds live in trees.

3. The deer ran fast.

4. Find a cloud.

Add the correct mark at the end of the statement.

5. The birds sang ____

Extension: Have children write an original sentence about something in the picture and add the correct mark at the end.

Name: Date:

ENDING WITH A QUESTION MARK

Remember

A sentence that asks something is a question.
A question ends with a question mark.

How many ducks are in the pond **?**

Read each sentence.
Add the correct mark at the end.

1. Which is the mother duck ___
2. Where are the little ducklings going ___
3. Can you give each duckling a name ___
4. What does a duck eat ___
5. Do you like ducks ___

Extension: Have children write a question about ducks and use the correct end mark.

Name: ____________________ Date: ____________

STATEMENTS AND QUESTIONS

A statement tells something. I see a duck.

A question asks something. Where is the mother?

Pretend you see a duck.

Write a statement about a duck.

____

____

Pretend you meet a duck.

What would you ask it? Write a question.

____

____

Extension: Have children study the picture and write an original statement or question.

Words in Order

Remember

A sentence tells a whole thought.
The words in a sentence must be in order.

fed I chicks. the	I fed the chicks.
words out of order	**words in order**

The words for each sentence are out of order.
Write each sentence with words in order.

1. ate seeds. The chicks

____

2. chick One peeped.

____

Extension: Have children write a sentence with incorrect word order and then exchange it with a classmate. Have children write each other's sentences in the correct order.

Name: ______________________ Date: ______________

Mixed-Up Sentences

Remember

The words in a sentence must be in order.
sat in a tree. The bird

The bird sat in a tree.

The words for each sentence are out of order. Write each sentence with words in order.

1. digs a hole. A dog

2. went away. The ducks

Extension: Have children write a sentence about the cat in the picture.

Name: Date:

FINDING THE RIGHT ORDER

Remember

The words must be in the correct order.

The children saw butterflies two pretty.
words out of order

The children saw two pretty butterflies.
words in order

Draw a circle around the sentence with words in the right order.

1. A boy saw a butterfly yellow.
2. The butterfly away flew.
3. A girl found a red flower.
4. A butterfly black was there.

 Extension: Have children correct the order of 1, 2, and 4.

Name: Date:

SENTENCES IN ORDER

Remember

A sentence tells a whole thought.
The words must be in order.

children swim The today. **words out of order**

The children swim today. **words in order**

Circle the word groups that are not in order.

1. a lake. went to The children.
2. "We are going for a swim," they said.
3. children the lake. like The

Find the word groups you circled.
Put the words in order. Write each sentence.

Extension: Have children write sentences about someone who swims.

SENTENCES IN ORDER

What is the child saying?
Write the sentence in the right order.

The children will make a line.
The smallest child will be **1**.
The tallest child will be **5**.
Show the correct order.
Write **1, 2, 3, 4,** or **5** on
the line under each child.

Extension: Have children draw five trees in a row from the shortest to the tallest and write a complete sentence about the drawing.

Sentence Parts

Match each naming part with an action part to make a sentence.

Naming Part	Action Part
1. The animals	is winning the game.
2. The game	are playing.
3. The dog	is unhappy.
4. Checkers	is checkers.
5. The cat	is a game.

Extension: Have children write an original sentence about something in the picture and add the correct mark at the end of the statement.

Name: Date:

The Naming Part

Remember

A sentence has a naming part.

The children play together.

The naming part is: **The children.**

Circle the naming part in the sentence.

1. The day is rainy.
2. The children play inside.
3. They are playing a game.
4. Jane will win the game.
5. Many children like games.

 Extension: Have children write a sentence and tell the naming part.

Name: Date:

THE ACTION PART

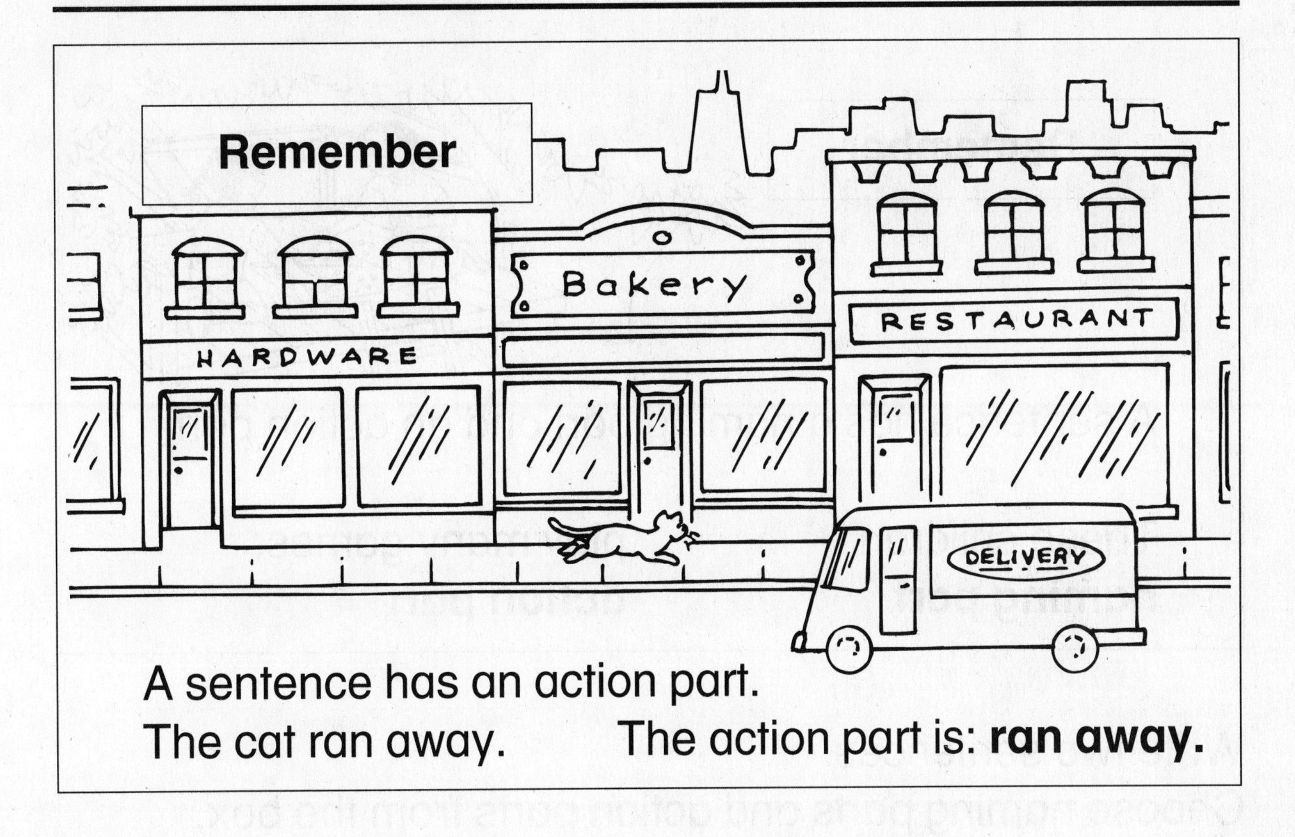

Remember

A sentence has an action part.
The cat ran away. The action part is: **ran away.**

Draw a line under the action part of the sentence.

1. The cat ran fast.
2. The cat saw new things.
3. A hat flew by.
4. He found a friend.
5. A girl gave him some fish.

Extension: Have children name two actions of a cat, for example, purr and scratch.

Name: ______________________ Date: ______________

NAMING AND ACTION PARTS

Remember

A sentence has a naming part and an action part.

These children	play many games.
naming part	**action part**

Write two sentences.
Choose naming parts and action parts from the box.

The children	took a turn.
Each child	found a game.

1. ____________________________________

2. ____________________________________

Extension: Give children a naming part or an action part of a sentence. Have children complete it.

SENTENCE PARTS IN ORDER

What does a cat like? Draw a picture of a cat and something it likes, such as a string, a ball, or a fish.

Write a sentence about your picture.

Extension: Have the children make up stories about their pictures.

Name: ______________________ Date: ______________

USING AND

This sentence tells about two animals.
Write the names of the animals.

1. The sheep and the lamb ate grass.

______________ ______________

This sentence names two actions.
Write the words that tell what the animal did.

2. The rooster marched and crowed.

______________ ______________

Extension: Have children name two new animals and two new actions.

Name: ______________________ Date: ______________

NAMING PARTS WITH AND

Remember

Two sentences may name the same action.

You can join the sentences. Use **and**.

Bees landed on flowers.

Butterflies landed on flowers.

Bees **and** butterflies landed on flowers.

Join the two sentences. Use **and**.

1. Lori dug in the dirt. Kim dug in the dirt.

____

2. An ant walked by. A beetle walked by.

____

Extension: Have children complete the sentence, "Flowers and trees . . ."

Name: ____________________ Date: ____________________

ACTION PARTS WITH AND

Remember

Two sentences may tell about the same person or thing. You can join the two sentences. Use **and**.

The cat runs. The cat jumps.
The cat runs **and** jumps.

Join the sentences. Use **and**.

1. The dog watches. The dog barks.

____

____

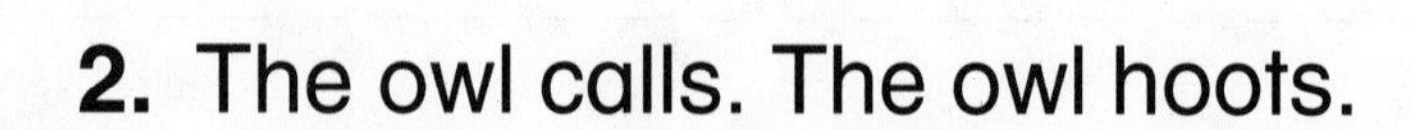

2. The owl calls. The owl hoots.

____

____

Extension: Have children supply two new actions for the dog, the owl, and the rabbits.

Name: Date:

Sentences with AND

Remember

You can join sentences that name the same person or thing. You can join sentences that name the same action. Use **and** to join the sentences.

We play **and** learn. My friends **and** I draw pictures.

Finish the sentence. Write the naming part that fits the action.

The sun and the moon Trees and flowers

1. ______________________ grow.

Finish the sentence. Name two actions for the animal.

fly and sing	buzz and sting

2. Bees ______________________.

Extension: Have children draw a picture of two things on the earth they like and write sentences about them.

Name: ______________________ Date: ______________________

WRITING SENTENCES WITH AND

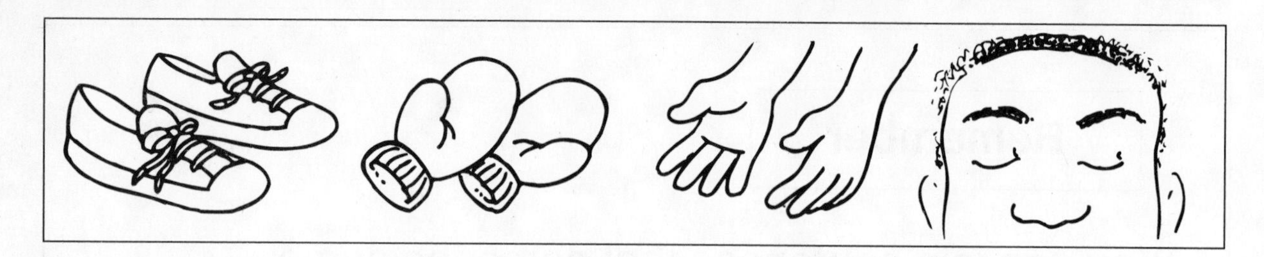

1. Write a sentence about two things that come in pairs.

2. Write a sentence about two things children often do.

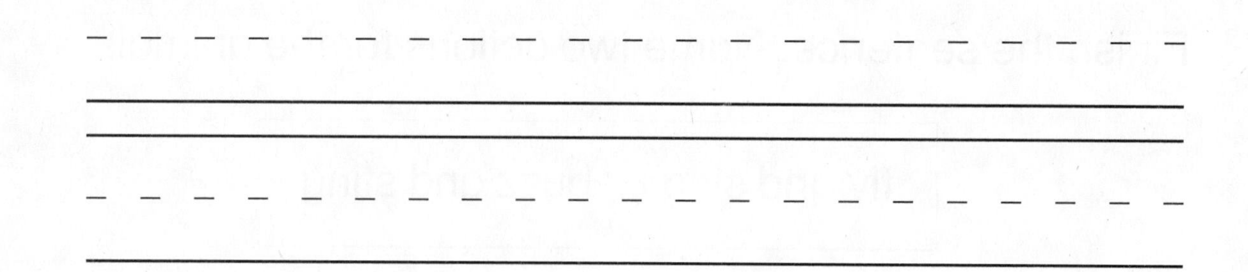

Extension: Have children make drawings for their sentences. Invite them to use *and* in both the naming and action parts of their sentences.

Name: ______________________ Date: ______________

NAMING WORDS

Remember

Some words name people.

Circle the words that name children.

The cat belongs to the girl.

The boy likes the cat.

The children play with the cat.

The brother has a car.

His sister has a truck.

Do the children play?

Extension: Ask children to make up their own sentences about people.

WORDS THAT NAME CHILDREN

Remember

Some words name children. **girl** **boy** **child** **children** **baby**

Choose a word from the box. Write it under the picture.

boy	girl	baby	children

1. 

2. 

3. 

4. 

Extension: Have children draw a picture of two children doing something together.

Name: ____________________ Date: ____________________

Words that Name People

Remember

Some words name people.

woman **man** **mother** **father**

A **woman** saw a cat.
A **man** saw a cat.

My **mother** saw a cat.
My **father** saw a cat.

Circle the word that names each picture.

1. 

man mother woman

2. 

father woman man

3. 

mother father woman

4. 

mother father man

Extension: Have children tell who saw the cat.

Name: Date:

WORDS THAT NAME PETS

Remember

Some words name pets.

dog **rabbit** **mouse** **cat**

Write the name of the pet.

1. A ______________ is playing with a [ball].

2. A ______________ is eating   .

3. A ______________ is playing with  .

4. A ______________ is sitting in a  .

Extension: Have children name the most unusual pets they have ever seen.

Name: ______________________ Date: ______________

WORDS THAT NAME PEOPLE IN A FAMILY

Each person in the family is carrying a pet.
Use the words in the box to complete each sentence.

1. The ______________ is carrying an ______.

2. The ______________ is carrying a ______.

3. The ______________ is carrying a ______.

4. The ______________ is carrying the ______.

Extension: Have children tell which pets they would pick for their own.

Name: ______________________ Date: ______________

MORE NAMING WORDS

Remember

Words name things.

Circle the word in each group that names one thing in each picture.

1. green grass big
2. run tree the

3. are apple red
4. best take basket

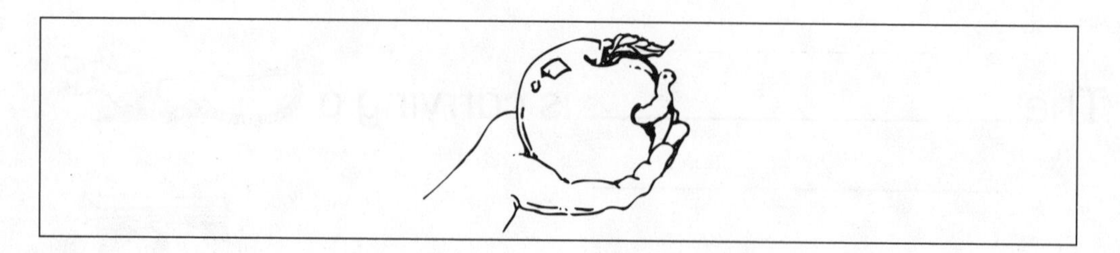

5. worm wish small
6. hand big hard

 Extension: Have children name a thing and draw a picture of it.

Name: Date:

WORDS THAT NAME PLACES

Remember

Some words name places.

house **home** **sky**

Write the name of each place in the picture.
Choose a word from the word box.

mountain	house	hill	sky	pond

1. ____________ 2. ____________

3. ____________ 4. ____________

5. ____________

Extension: Have children color their pictures.

WORDS THAT NAME THINGS

Remember Some words name things.

balloon **kite**

Find each thing in the picture. Color it.

1. Find the clouds. Color the clouds gray.
2. Find the hat. Color the hat blue.
3. Find the ball. Color the ball orange.
4. Find the balloon. Color the balloon red.
5. Find the kite. Color the kite purple.
6. Find the cup. Color the cup yellow.

Extension: Have children tell about their experiences on a windy day.

Name: Date:

NAMES OF PLACES AND THINGS

Remember

Some words name places.
Some words name things.

cloud **thing** sky **place**

Draw a circle around the words that name places and things.

1. A bus drove away.
2. It went up the hill.
3. The car is next to a house.
4. There are trees next to the house.
5. The children see a train.
6. The train will go to the city.

Extension: Have children tell about trips they have made by bus, car, or train.

Name: Date:

FINDING PLACES AND THINGS

Remember

Some words name places. **sky**
Some words name things. **cloud**

Look at the picture. Write the number of places you see.
Write the number of things you see.

1. How many stations?

2. How many hats?

3. How many flowers?

4. How many cats?

Extension: Have children identify the numbers for the women, the dog, and the hill.

PEOPLE, PLACES, AND THINGS

Remember

Some words name **people, places,** or **things.**
man girl school hat

Circle the word that names the picture.

1.

hat hop man house

2.

sit girl said school

3.

fan mop man hat

4.

goat girl get school

4 Level 2

Extension: Have children make up a sentence using one of the nouns on the page.

Name: ______________________ Date: ______________________

MORE WORDS THAT NAME PEOPLE

Remember

Some words name **people**.

son mother father grandmother

One word is underlined in each sentence.
Write another word to name the same person.
Choose a word from the box. Write it on the lines.

boy	grandma	dad	mom

1. The son says, "I want to walk in the rain."

2. The father says, "It is windy out."

3. The mother says, "You might get cold."

4. The grandmother says, "Wear a raincoat."

Extension: Have children make up a new dialogue for the story.

Name: ____________________ Date: ____________________

MORE WORDS THAT NAME PLACES

Remember

Some words name **places**.

lake **sky** **hill** **bay**

Read the sentences below.
Fill in the blanks with words from the box.

1. There are rowboats down by the ____________________.

2. There is a tree on the ____________________.

3. There are clouds in the ____________________.

4. There is a sailboat on the ____________________.

Extension: Have children name a rhyming word for each word.

MORE WORDS THAT NAME THINGS

Read the animal facts.
Draw lines to the correct animals.
Use the pictures to help.

Fact	**Animal**
1. It is the biggest.	bear
2. It likes mud.	whale
3. It sleeps all winter.	goose
4. It lays eggs.	goat
5. It may live on mountains.	pig

 Extension: Have children name one thing each animal likes to eat.

Name: _______________ Date: _______________

People, Places, and Things

Remember

Words can name **people, places,** or **things.**

People:	girl	mother	boy
Places:	home	school	store
Things:	bird	tree	hat

Choose a word from the box to complete each sentence. Write it on the line.

1. A _______________ rode the bus.

2. A bird was in the _______________.

3. The girl wore a red _______________.

4. The _______________ is far from home.

5. The _______________ is pretty.

Extension: Have the children pick a category and write a story using all three words.

PROPER NOUNS

Remember

Nouns are words that name people, places, and things.
Proper nouns name special people, places, and things.

Read each sentence.
Find the word that names a special person, place, or thing.
Draw a line under it.

1. Tony has a garden.
2. He calls it New Town Garden.
3. His brother Pete helps him.
4. They sell flowers in New Town.
5. The brothers live near Water Bay.

Extension: Have children write their own name and the name of their town in a sentence.

Name: ______________________ Date: ______________

NAMING SPECIAL PEOPLE

Remember

Words that name people are nouns.
Special names begin with a capital letter.

Look at the picture of Jani's family.
It shows Jani with her father, her mother,
her brother, and her sister.

Write their special names.

1. The father's name is ______________.
2. The mother's name is ______________.
3. The brother's name is ______________.
4. The baby's name is ______________.

Extension: Have children make a list of the names of the members of their own or another family.

Name: ________________________ Date: ________________

DAYS OF THE WEEK

Remember

Special names begin with a capital letter.

The name of each day of the week begins with a capital letter.

Use Maria's list to help you answer each question. Write the name of each day on the line.

1. When will Maria weed the garden?

   ____

2. When will Maria go to the flower shop?

   ____

3. When will Grandpa visit?

   ____

4. When will Maria have an art class?

   ____

 Extension: Have children make their own weekly schedule.

Name: ____________________ Date: ____________

Names of Months

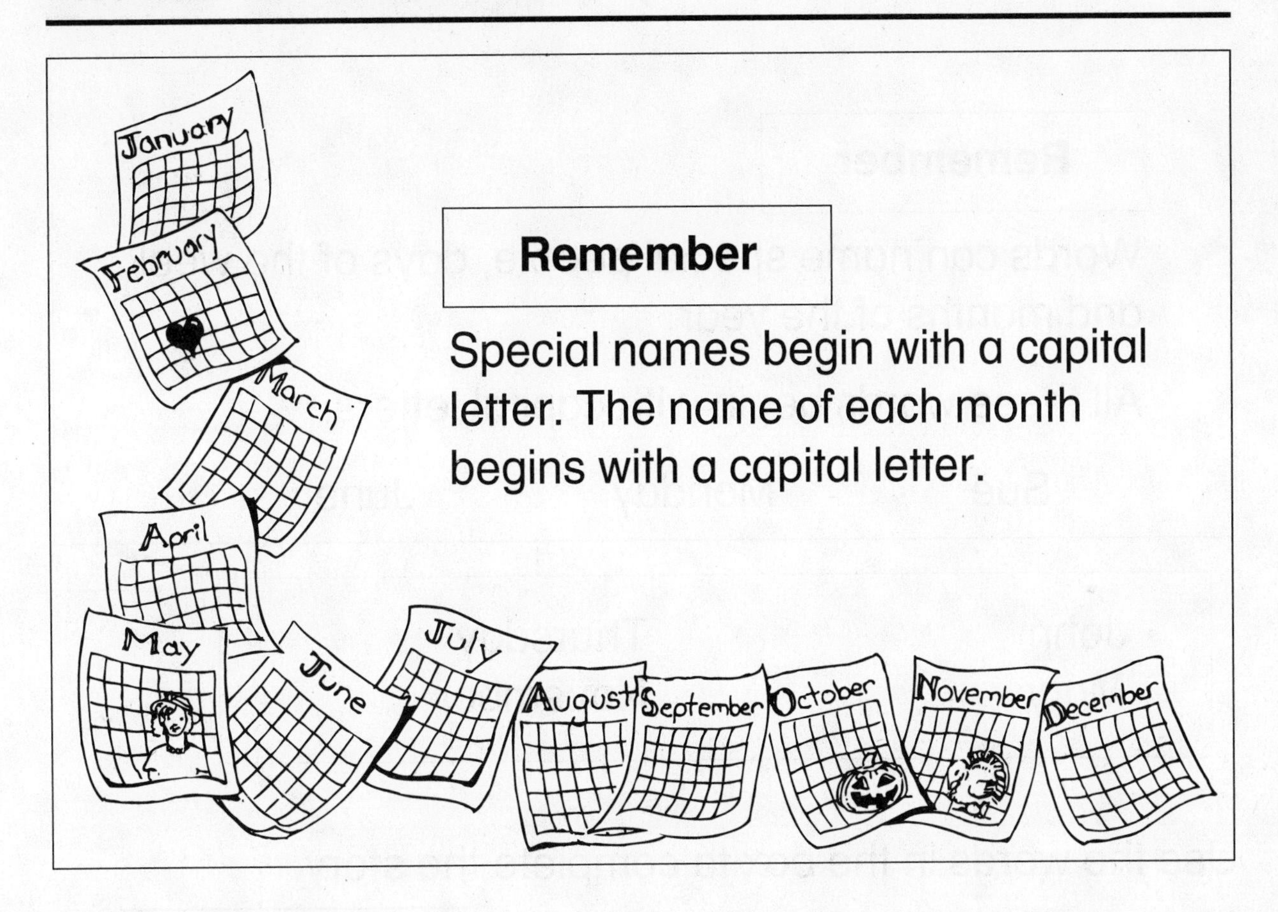

Remember

Special names begin with a capital letter. The name of each month begins with a capital letter.

Look at the calendar.
Write the name of the month that matches the holiday.

1. Thanksgiving

2. Halloween

3. Mother's Day

4. Valentine's Day

Extension: Have children write the name of the month when their favorite holiday is celebrated.

Special Names, Days, Months

Remember

Words can name special people, days of the week, and months of the year.

All these words begin with capital letters.

Sue Monday June

John	Thursday
Mary	November

Use the words in the box to complete the story.

1. Thanksgiving Day is always on a ______________.

2. It is always in the month of ______________.

3. ______________ plays Squanto in the Thanksgiving play.

4. ______________ dresses up like a Pilgrim.

Extension: Have children tell a story that takes place in June.

Name: ______________________ Date: ______________

MORE THAN ONE

Remember

A noun names a person, place, or thing.
Some nouns name more than one.

three **trees** one **boy**

Follow the directions. Draw a picture in each box.

1. One snowman

2. Two mittens

3. Three hats

4. Four boots

Extension: Have children name things that come in pairs, for example gloves, shoes.

Name: ______________________ Date: ______________________

PLURAL NOUNS

Remember

Nouns can name one person, place, or thing.
Some nouns name more than one.

one **dog** and one **cat** two **dogs** and three **cats**

Find the people, places, and things in each picture.
Circle the pictures that show more than one.

Extension: Have children draw a picture to show one and more than one of an item.

Name: ______________________ Date: ______________________

NOUNS FOR MORE THAN ONE

Remember

Some nouns name one. girl

Some nouns name more than one. girls

Read the story.
Draw a line under the nouns that name more than one.

1. The girl had blocks.
2. She shared them with friends.
3. The girls built a tall tower.
4. Then they built more tall towers.
5. What will the girls make next?

Extension: Have children write a sentence about a time they built something with their friends.

Name: ______________________ Date: ______________

ADDING *s* TO MAKE PLURALS

Remember

A plural noun names more than one. mitten

\+ **s**

Add **s** to form the plural of many nouns. mittens

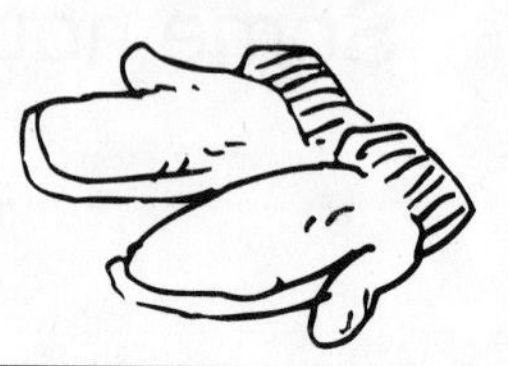

Add **s** to each word in the box.
Complete the sentences.
Write the correct word on the line.

street	brother	hat	night

1. Snow fell for two ______________.

2. It covered the ______________.

3. Joy played with her ______________.

4. They all wore ______________.

Extension: Have children draw a picture of a child dressed for the snow.

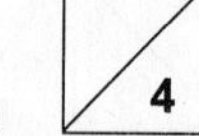

Name: ______________________ Date: ______________

WRITING PLURAL NOUNS

Remember

Some nouns name more than one thing.
Add **s** to form the plural of many nouns.

flower
+ **s**
flowers

Al's mother made a list for the store.
Some of the words are plural nouns.

Circle the plural nouns that end in **s**.
Write the plural nouns on the lines.

beans
tea
flowers
limes
jam
peas
butter

Extension: Have children add items to the grocery list that are plural nouns ending in **s**.

PLURAL NOUNS

Remember

Plural nouns name more than one thing.
Many plural nouns end in **s**.
Some plural nouns do not end in **s.**

duck **ducks**
The plural ends in **s**.

goose **geese**
The word changes for the plural noun.

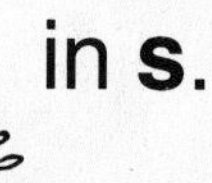

Write the plural for each animal name.

1. kitten ________________

2. goose ________________

3. bug ________________

4. mouse ________________

Extension: Have children write the singular and plural forms of other animal names.

Name: ____________________ Date: ____________

SPECIAL PLURALS

Remember

Some plural nouns do not end in **s**.

one	child	man
more than one	children	men

Write the word from the box that names these people.

1. grown up boys ____________________

2. more than one child ____________________

Write the words from the box that complete the sentence.

3. The ____________________ drive the ____________________ to school.

4 Level 3

Extension: Have children make up a slogan for safety using the word *children*.

MORE SPECIAL PLURALS

Remember

Some nouns do not form the plural by adding **s**.

tooth teeth foot feet

Write the word from the box that completes each sentence.

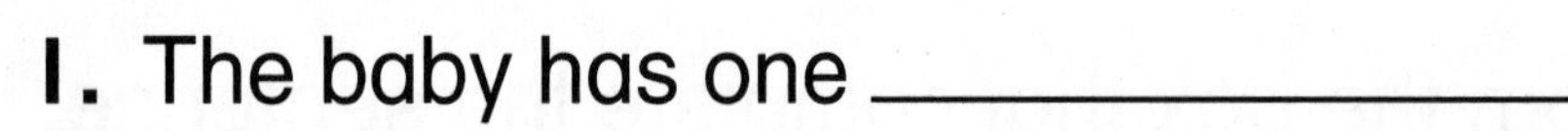

1. The baby has one ________.

2. Later, the baby will have many ________.

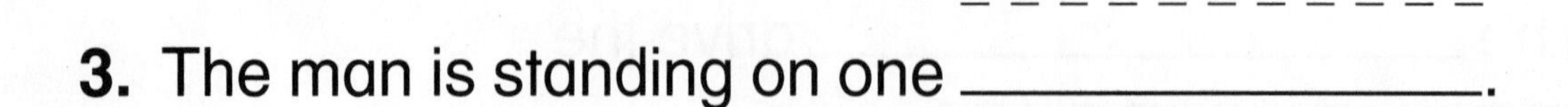

3. The man is standing on one ________.

4. He will stand on two ________.

 Extension: Have children create posters about brushing their teeth.

PRACTICE WITH PLURAL NOUNS

Write the plural form of each noun.

1. mouse ________________

2. hen ________________

3. goose ________________

4. pig ________________

Extension: Have children act out a barnyard scene by playing each of the animals.

Name: ______________________ Date: ______________________

PLURAL NOUNS

Use the words in the box to complete the poster.

pigs	ducklings	ducks	horses	geese

Come to the fair!

Hear the ______________ honk

and the ______________ oink.

Ride the ______________.

Feed the ______________ and

their ______________.

Extension: Have children write a letter telling about the poster they created for the fair.

Name: ____________________ Date: ____________________

WRITING SPECIAL NAMES

Remember

A word that names a person is a noun.
Special names begin with a **capital letter**.

Mr. James

Nira

Make a list of special names.
Write a name for each person on the list.

1. your school principal ____________________

2. your teacher ____________________

3. a friend ____________________

4. a pet ____________________

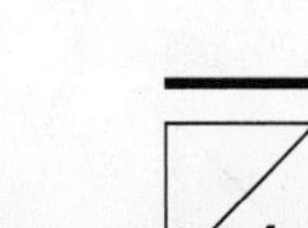

Extension: Have children list the special names of people in their family.

Name: ______________________ Date: ______________

NAMING WORDS

Remember

The name of a person begins with a **capital letter**.

Humpty Dumpty

Polly

Write each name correctly on the lines.
Remember to use capital letters.

1. wendy darling ______________________

2. mary poppins ______________________

3. jack horner ______________________

4. peter pan ______________________

Extension: Have children recite the nursery rhymes that name the people in the lesson.

Name: Date:

Names of Days and Months

Remember

The name of each day begins with a **capital letter**.

Monday Thursday

The name of each month begins with a **capital letter**.

March September

Circle each word that should begin with a capital letter.

1. Jack and Jill went up the hill on monday.
2. Humpty Dumpty sat on a wall on saturday.
3. Tom Tucker sang for his supper in may.
4. Miss Muffet sat on a tuffet in june.
5. Polly put the kettle on in december.

Extension: Have children recite nursery rhymes they know.

Name: ______________________ Date: ______________________

NAMING MORE THAN ONE

Remember

Some nouns name more than one.
Add **s** to a noun to name more than one.

brother
sister

brothers
sisters

Add **s** to each word to name more than one.
Write the new word on the line.

1. bird ______________________

2. flower ______________________

3. rose ______________________

4. animal ______________________

Extension: Have children choose one word from the list. Have them draw pictures of one and more than one. Have them label the drawings.

Name: ______________________ Date: ______________

More Plural Nouns

Remember

Some nouns that name more than one do not end in **s**.

One	mouse	goose	child	tooth
More than one	mice	geese	children	teeth

Complete each sentence. Use a word from the box that means more than one.

1. Many ______________________ flew by.

2. The ______________________ are singing songs.

3. Take care of your ______________________.

4. Some ______________________ eat corn.

Extension: Have children write a sentence for one of the plurals in the box.

Name: ____________________ Date: ____________________

NOUNS THAT NAME AN OWNER

Remember

A noun can show who owns something.
A noun can show what owns something.
Nouns that show the owner end in **'s**.

Peter

jacket

Peter + **'s**

Peter's jacket

Read each sentence.
Find the noun that shows who owns something.
Draw a circle around the word.

1. Peter's mother said, "Go and play."
2. "Stay away from Mr. MacGregor's garden."
3. That was Mother's rule.
4. Look at Flopsy's flower.
5. Look at Mopsy's butterfly.

Extension: Have children draw a picture of Flopsy's flower or Mopsy's butterfly and label it.

NOUNS THAT SHOW WHO OWNS IT

Remember

Some nouns name people.
You can show who owns something.
Add **'s** to the name.

Who owns a rabbit?
Todd owns a rabbit.
Todd + **'s**

Todd**'s** rabbit

Each child owns a pet.
Show who owns each pet.
Add **'s** to the name.

1. Nan owns a frog.

________________ frog

2. Bob owns a fish.

________________ fish

3. Jed owns a cat.

________________ cat

4. Pam owns a dog.

________________ dog

Extension: Have children write their own name with an *'s* to show something they own.

NOUNS THAT NAME OWNERS

Remember

Some nouns name animals.
You can show that an animal owns something.
Add **'s** to the name.

Write who owns each thing.
Add **'s** to the name of the animal.

1. The hole belongs to a rabbit.

____________ hole

2. The dam belongs to a beaver.

____________ dam

3. The nest belongs to a bird.

____________ nest

4. The den belongs to a fox.

____________ den

Extension: Have children write a sentence for one of the possessive nouns.

More Nouns that Show Owners

Remember

Nouns name people and animals.
You can show that a person or an animal owns something.
Add **'s** to the name.

Write the noun that shows the owner.

1. Jill's bird sings. ______________ bird
2. Jill likes the bird's song. ______________ song

3. Mike's rabbit has a cage. ______________ rabbit
4. Mike cleans the rabbit's cage. ______________ cage

Extension: Have children write possessive nouns to show that a boy owns a fish and the fish has a bowl.

WHO OWNS IT?

Remember

You can show who or what owns something.
Add **'s** to the name of a person or an animal.

Who owns it?
Write the name of the owner.
Choose a name from the box. Add **'s**.

Mary

mouse

King Cole

cat

1. Whose fiddle? ______________________
2. Whose clock? ______________________
3. Whose garden? ______________________
4. Whose bowl? ______________________

Extension: Have children recite the nursery rhymes referred to in each item.

Name: ____________________ Date: ____________________

Action Words

Remember

Some words show action.
These words are **action verbs.**

Look at the picture. Read each sentence. Circle the action verb.

1. The cow looks.

2. The horse eats.

3. Four legs stand tall.

4. One nose sniffs the air.

5. One bird flies.

6. Two geese talk.

Extension: Have children draw a picture of an animal doing something. Then, ask them to write a sentence for the picture, and circle the action verb.

Name: ______________________ Date: ______________________

ACTION VERBS IN SCHOOL

Remember

Words that show actions are verbs.
Some verbs name actions in school.

Read the sentences.
Write the action verb in each sentence.

1. Jess walks to school. ______________________

2. She talks to her friends. ______________________

3. They find a spider. ______________________

4. They write a story. ______________________

Extension: Have children write a sentence that tells about the spider.
Have them identify the action verb.

ACTION VERBS AT HOME

Remember

Words that show action are verbs.
Some action verbs name actions at home.

The children help at home. help

Write the action verb for each sentence.
Choose a verb from the box.

feeds	need	walks	clean

1. The pets ______________ care.

2. The boy ______________ the cat.

3. The girl ______________ the dog.

4. The children ______________ the bird cage.

Extension: Have children tell how they help at home. Have them identify the action verbs they use.

Name: ______________________ Date: ______________________

VERBS AT A BALL GAME

Remember

Words that show action are verbs.
Some action verbs name actions at a ball game.

Match the person with the action.
Choose a verb from the box.
Write the action verb.

waits	throws	hits	catches

1. The pitcher ______________________.

2. The catcher ______________________.

3. The batter ______________________.

4. The fielder ______________________.

Extension: Have children tell what the fans do. Have them identify the action verbs in their sentences.

Name: ______________________ Date: ______________________

ACTION VERBS AT A CIRCUS

Remember

Words that show action are verbs.
Some action verbs show actions at a circus.

Look at the picture.
Choose a verb from the box.
Write an action verb in each sentence.

rides	walks	holds	wears

1. The clown ______________ a balloon.

2. The man ______________ a hat.

3. The woman ______________ a horse.

4. The girl ______________ on the wire.

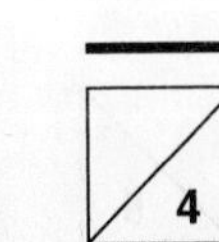

Extension: Have children draw a circus picture. Ask them to tell about the picture, and help them identify the action verbs they use.

Name: _______________ Date: _______________

Action Happening Now

Remember

Words that name actions are action verbs.
Some verbs tell what is happening now.

We **watch** the animals.
When do we watch? We watch **now**.

Each sentence has an action verb.
The verb tells what is happening now.
Draw a circle around each action verb.

1. A lamb eats grass.
2. A mouse nibbles corn.
3. A bear finds honey.
4. A caterpillar walks on a leaf.
5. A butterfly flies away.

Extension: Have children draw a picture of an animal doing something. Then have them write the action verb that tells what the animal is doing.

Name: ____________________ Date: ____________________

VERBS TELL WHAT HAPPENS NOW

Remember

Verbs name actions.
A verb can name an action that happens now.

Joey **plays** with his dog. When does Joey play?
He plays now.

Write the action verb on the line.

1. Joey pats his dog's head.

____

2. The dog runs for a ball.

____

3. Joey loves his pet.

____

4. Joey and his dog play.

____

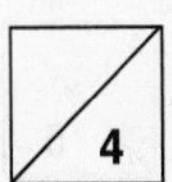

Extension: Have children tell what happens when Joey and his dog play in the park. Have them identify the action verb in each sentence.

Name: Date:

Verbs Can Tell About One

Remember

Some verbs tell about one person or thing.
These verbs end in **s**.

Find the verb in each sentence.
The verb tells about one person or thing. It ends in **s**.
Draw a circle around each verb.

1. The mouse lives in a cage.

2. It likes seeds.

3. Amy feeds the mouse.

4. She gives the mouse a wheel.

5. The wheel turns.

Extension: Have children tell what happens when the mouse gets out of the cage. Have them identify the action words they use.

Name: ______________________ Date: ______________

VERBS FOR MORE THAN ONE

Remember

Some verbs tell about more than one person or thing.
These verbs do not end in **s**.

The boys **like** caterpillars.
How many boys? more than one
like verb does not end in **s**

Each verb tells about more than one.
These verbs do not end in **s**.
Write the verb in each sentence.

1. Caterpillars live on leaves. ______________

2. They eat all day. ______________

3. Caterpillars change. ______________

4. Soon butterflies fly away. ______________

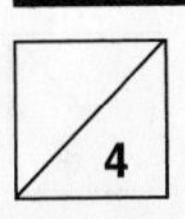

Extension: Have children draw butterflies and write one or more sentences that tell about the butterflies. Have children identify each action verb.

Verbs for One and More than One

Remember

Verbs that tell about one end in **s.**
Verbs that tell about more than one do not end in **s.**

The girl **likes** animals.
One girl verb ends in **s**

The girls **like** animals.
More than one girl
verb does not end in **s**

Look at the verb in each sentence.
Does it tell about one or more than one?
Draw a circle around **one** or **more than one**.

1. Lisa **wants** a pony. one more than one

2. Many children **like** cats. one more than one

3. Two girls **find** alligators. one more than one

4. Jenny **sees** a lamb. one more than one

Extension: Have children write one sentence about one friend and another about two friends. Compare the two verbs.

Name: ____________________ Date: ____________

Is and *Are*

Remember

Verbs can tell about something that happens now.
The verbs **is** and **are** tell about something now.

Hector **is** a pig.

Write the verb in each sentence.

1. He is in the mud. ____________
2. Mud is dirty. ____________
3. Dirty days are happy days. ____________
4. Hector is happy. ____________

Extension: Have children draw a picture of Hector and write a sentence about him.

Name: ____________________ Date: ____________________

VERBS *IS* AND *ARE*

Remember

Verbs can tell about something now.
Two verbs that tell about something now are **is** and **are.**

The verbs **is** and **are** tell about something now.
Circle the verb in each sentence.

1. The animals are outside.

2. The sheep is beautiful.

3. The rabbits are small.

4. The mouse is tiny.

5. Who is silly?

6. The bird is happy.

Extension: Have children write a sentence about the bird.

Name: ____________________ Date: ____________________

USING IS

Remember

Some verbs tell about one person or thing.
The verb **is** tells about one person or thing.

Read each sentence.
Draw a line under the verb.

1. My friend is funny.

2. She is in the house.

3. What is her name?

4. Her name is Alex.

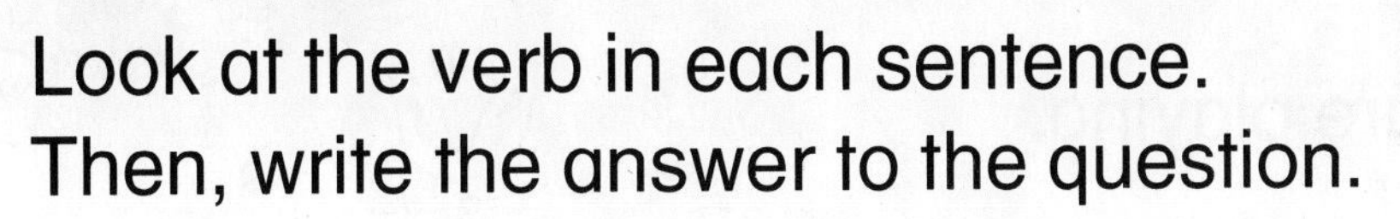

Look at the verb in each sentence.
Then, write the answer to the question.

5. Which verb tells about one?

____

Extension: Have children write a sentence about a friend and use *is* in the sentence.

Name: ______________________ Date: ______________________

USING ARE

Remember

Some verbs tell about more than one person or thing.
The verb **are** tells about more than one person or thing.

Read each sentence.
Draw a line under the verb.

1. The rabbits are black and white.
2. They are happy in the grass.
3. Some rabbits are eating.
4. Some rabbits are playing.

Look at the verb in each sentence.
Then, write the answer to the question.

5. Which verb tells about more than one?

____

Extension: Have children tell how many black and how many white rabbits there are. Sentences begin: "There are"....

USING IS AND ARE

Remember

The verb **is** tells about one person or thing.
The verb **are** tells about more than one person or thing.

Read each sentence. Circle the verb.

1. Four green frogs are in the pond.
2. Three frogs are on the lily pads.
3. Where is the other frog?
4. It is under the water.

Look at the picture. There are no frogs in the picture.

5. Draw four frogs in the picture.
Put them where they belong.

Extension: Have children write a sentence about another animal that could live near a pond.

Name: ______________________ Date: ______________________

ACTIONS IN THE PAST

Remember

Words that name actions are **verbs.** Verbs can name actions that happened in the past.

The sentences tell a story. Each verb tells an action that happened in the past. Write the verb on the line.

1. The king waited for his friend.

   ____

2. The friend came late.

   ____

3. She looked in the woods for a gift.

   ____

4. At last she found one for the king.

   ____

Extension: Have children tell what the king might say when his friend finally arrrives.

Name: ____________________ Date: ____________________

Actions in the Past

Remember

An action verb can tell what is happening now.
An action verb can tell what happened in the past.

Rain **cleans** the air.
Action verb: **cleans**
When? **Now**

Rain **cleaned** the air.
Action verb: **cleaned**
When? **In the past**

Read the sentences and find each action verb.
Which verbs tell about actions in the past?
Write only the verbs that tell about past actions.

1. The rain started. ____________________

2. It falls all day. ____________________

3. Suddenly the rain stopped. ____________________

4. We smelled the air outside. ____________________

Extension: Have children write one sentence to complete the story. Have them identify each action verb as present or past.

Name: ______________________ Date: ______________

Actions in the Past

Remember

Some verbs tell about actions that happened in the past.
These verbs are called past-tense verbs.

Add **ed** to form **past-tense verbs**.

peck pecked

Add **ed** to each verb. Write the new verb on the line.

1. want

   The chicken ____________________ to tell the king.

2. ask

   The cock ____________________ for good news.

3. warn

   The turkey ____________________ all the birds.

4. wait

   The fox ____________________ for some food.

Extension: Have children write one sentence to tell something they did yesterday. Have them identify each action verb as past tense.

Name: ______________________ Date: ______________________

Past-Tense Verbs with *ed*

Remember

Some verbs show action that happened in the past.
Many past-tense verbs end in **ed.**

Many verbs that show past-tense action end in **ed.**
Draw a circle around the past-tense verbs that end in **ed.**

1. The baby sat on the floor.

2. He watched the snow.

3. Then the baby crawled to his mom.

4. He sat on her lap.

5. The baby smiled at his mom.

Extension: Have the children tell what the baby did next.

Name: ______________________ Date: ______________________

VERBS ABOUT ACTIONS IN THE PAST

Remember

Past-tense verbs tell about actions in the past.
Add **ed** to the verb to form the past tense.

Where does each action verb belong? Write each verb in the chart.

turn	turned	buzzed	buzz
listen	listened	asked	ask

	PRESENT-TENSE VERBS	PAST-TENSE VERBS
1.	______	______
2.	______	______
3.	______	______
4.	______	______

Extension: Have children use these present- and past-tense verbs in sentences.

SPECIAL FORMS FOR PAST TENSE

Remember

Most past-tense verbs end in **ed**.
Some verbs have special forms to tell about the past.

The verb in each sentence tells about the past.
Write the verb on the line.

1. My friend lived on my street. ____________
2. He moved to a new city. ____________
3. A letter came from me. ____________
4. My friend was happy. ____________

Extension: Have children write a letter to someone they know.

COME AND CAME

Remember

Some verbs show actions that are happening now.
Some verbs show past actions.
Use **come** for actions that are happening now.
Use **came** for past actions.

Find the verb in each sentence. Circle the verb.

1. Come to a big party in the city.
2. The police officers come first.
3. The fire fighters come on the train.
4. Yesterday, the band members came by bus.

Write the two different verbs you circled on the lines.

5. ______________________ ______________________

Extension: Have children volunteer a sentence that uses *come* or *comes.*

FORM FOR THE PAST: CAME

Remember

Some verbs do not form the past by adding **ed**.
Use **come** to tell about actions that happen now.
Use **came** to tell about past actions.

Write the verb.

1. The knight came to visit. ____________

2. He came to the home of the king. ____________

3. Royal visitors came with him. ____________

4. They came late at night. ____________

Extension: Have children tell what the knight and the royal visitors did when they came to visit.

Name: ______________________ Date: ______________

USE COME OR CAME

Remember

Use **come** to tell about actions that happen now.
Use **came** to tell about past actions.

Use **come**, **comes**, or **came** in each sentence.
Underline the correct verb.

1. We often (come, comes) to the mountains.

2. We (comes, came) early last spring.

3. Summer (came, come) in June.

4. Many people (comes, come) to the mountains in the summer.

5. My friend (comes, come) every year.

Extension: Have students write a letter inviting someone to come and visit the class.

Name: ______________________ Date: ____________

PAST-TENSE VERBS

Remember

Some verbs change their form when they tell about the past.
The past tense of **come** is **came**.

Find each sentence with a past-tense verb.
Circle the first letter of that sentence.

1. We came early to the pool on Friday.
2. Sam comes late every Saturday.
3. Everyone came early on Sunday.
4. Tuesday he came early.

Write the first letters you circled.

5. ______ ______ ______

Use the letters to spell a word that answers the question.

6. How was the water in the pool? ____________

Extension: Have children make up a sentence about an interesting person who came to dinner.

Name: _______________ Date: _______________

USE SAY OR SAID

Remember

Use **say** to tell about someone talking right now.
Use **said** to tell about someone talking in the past.

Circle **say** or **said** to complete each sentence.

1. Dad _______ the baby cried all day yesterday.
say said

2. Now Ann and Andy _______ the baby is crying again.
say said

3. The baby _______ her first word last week.
say said

4. Now, Dad and the baby _______ the word together.
say said

5. Yesterday, Mom _______, "The baby is growing fast."
say said

 Extension: Have children use **say** and **said** in oral sentences.

USING SAY AND SAYS

Remember

Some verbs tell about actions that are happening now. Use **say** or **says** for actions that are happening now.

Write **say** or **says** to complete each sentence.

1. Dad ____________________ we can go skating with him.

2. Bill ____________________ that he needs help skating.

3. Kim and I ____________________ we need help, too.

4. Dad ____________________ he can help us all.

5. We ____________________, "Thanks, Dad!"

Extension: Have children use **say** and **says** in oral sentences.

Name: ______________________ Date: ______________

USING SAID

Remember

Some verbs have special forms to show an action in the past.
Use **said** to show an action in the past.

Read each sentence.
If the action happened in the past, write the word **said** on the line.
If it is happening now, do not write anything.

1. Barb ______________ she was sick yesterday.
2. Now she ______________ she feels well.
3. Tony ______________ he had a cold last week.
4. He ______________ he had to stay home from school.
5. Now he ______________ he still has a cough.

Extension: Have children use **said** to describe a conversation they had in the past.

Name: ______________________ Date: ______________

SAY OR SAID

Remember

Use **say** to tell about someone talking now.
Use **said** to tell about someone talking in the past.

Write **say**, **says**, or **said** to complete each sentence.

1. I wake up when Mom ______________________, "Rise and shine!"

2. I close my eyes and ______________________, "Just a little longer, please."

3. But yesterday, I ______________________, "Rise and shine."

4. Mom ______________________, "Just a little longer, please."

5. Then I ______________________, "Mom, you are silly!"

Extension: Have children use **say** and **said** in oral sentences.

Name: ______________________ Date: ______________

USING SAID IN STORIES

Remember

Said shows an action that happened in the past.
Most stories use **said** when people speak.

Mother **said** Little Red Riding Hood **said**

Read the story.
Write **said** on each line.

Mother __________, "Take this basket to Grandmother."

Little Red Riding Hood __________, "I love to visit Grandmother. I can walk through the woods."

Big Bad Wolf __________, "Hello, Red Riding Hood."

Little Red Riding Hood __________, "Grandmother, what big teeth you have!"

Extension: Have children take the wolf's part: The Wolf said, "The better to eat you with, my dear."

Name: ____________________ Date: ____________________

USING GO AND WENT

Remember

Some verbs have special forms for the past.
The past tense of **go** is **went**.

Read each sentence.
Draw a line under the past-tense verb.

1. The children went to the fair.

2. Jojo went to the ring.

3. The boys and girls go to school.

4. They went around the ring.

5. Circle the numbers of the sentences that have the past-tense verb **went**.

1 2 3 4

Extension: Have children name other animals and use them with **went** in a sentence.

Name: ______________________ Date: ______________________

USING GO FOR PRESENT TENSE

Remember

The verb **go** tells about actions that happen now.
Use **goes** when you tell about one person.
Use **go** when you tell about more than one person.

Look at the pictures.
Write **go** or **goes** in each sentence.

1. Pat ______________ for her  lesson.

2. Pete also ______________ today to play the .

3. Lee and Ann ______________ next for  lessons.

4. Who ______________ last to play the ?

Extension: Have children name an instrument to complete the sentence, "Today I go to play . . . ."

Name: ______________________ Date: ______________________

USE WENT FOR PAST TENSE

Remember

Some verbs have special forms for the past tense.
Use **went** for the past tense of **go**.

Fill in the missing verb.
Write the past tense form **went**.

1. Jason ______________ to see the fan.

2. Pam ______________ the next day.

3. Soon the whole class ______________ .

4. Our teachers ______________ with us.

5. Color the bands on the fan.
Use red for present tense.
Use blue for past tense.

Extension: Have children tell about something beautiful they went to see.

Name: ______________________ Date: ______________________

USING GO OR WENT

Remember

Use **go** to tell about actions that happen now.
Use **went** to tell about past actions.

Write **go** or **went** in each sentence.
Write **went** to tell about past actions.

1. Now, the children ______________ out.

2. Yesterday, Lily ______________ to see her friend.

3. The day before, Manny ______________, too.

4. Now, Janet and Lee ______________ for a walk.

5. Yesterday, Jasper ______________ to the pond.

Extension: Have children tell where they go each afternoon of the week.

Name: ______________________ Date: ______________

WRITING WITH GO AND WENT

Remember

Use past-tense verbs when you tell about something that already happened.
The children **went** out in the snow.

The sentences tell about an event.
Write **went** to tell about past actions.

1. Boys and girls ______________ to the top of the hill.

2. Each child ______________ down the hill on a sled.

3. Everyone ______________ down more than once.

4. Lee ______________ down on her sled five times.

Extension: Have children write a sentence telling why the boys and girls went home.

USING WAS AND WERE

Remember

Use **was** for one.
Use **were** for more than one.

Each sentence is missing a word.
Write **was** or **were** on the line.

1. Ducks ________________ swimming in the pond.

2. One duck ________________ looking for food.

3. His head ________________ under the water.

4. The other ducks ________________ hungry, too.

Extension: Have children draw a picture of one duck and tell what it was doing.

USING WAS

Remember

Use **was** when you tell about one person, animal, or thing.

Read each sentence.
If it tells about one person, animal, or thing, write the word **was** on the line. If it tells about more than one, do not write anything.

1. Greg's new pet ______________________ a kitten.

2. The kitten's name ______________________ Fred.

3. Fred ______________________ cute and furry.

4. He ______________________ silly, too.

5. Greg and his dad ______________________ happy to have Fred.

Extension: Have children use **was** in oral sentences.

Name: ________________ Date: ________________

USING WERE

Remember

Use the verb **was** for one. One child **was** the baker.

Use the verb **were** for more than one. Two children **were** helpers.

Draw a line under each verb.
Write the subject that names more than one.

1. Three eggs were fresh.

____

2. One dozen muffins were ready.

____

3. Two jars of jelly were on the table.

____

4. Four children were hungry.

____

Extension: Have children write a sentence beginning with **five** and using **were** as the verb.

Name: Date:

CHOOSING WAS OR WERE

Remember

Use **was** to tell about one.
Use **were** to tell about more than one.

Each sentence tells about one or more than one.
Write **was** or **were** on the line.

1. The dog ________________ swimming.

2. The flowers ________________ pretty.

3. The frogs ________________ jumping.

4. The cat ________________ in the tree.

Extension: Have children add something to the picture and write a sentence about it using **was** or **were**.

Name: ______________________ Date: ______________

USING *WAS* AND *WERE*

Remember

Use **was** and **were** to tell about the past.
Use **was** for one.
Use **were** for more than one.

Answer the questions to complete the story.
Use **was** and **were** in your sentences.

It was a day like any other. Then I saw the egg. It cracked open.

What came out?

____

Where did it come from?

____

What color was it?

____

What happened next?

____

 Extension: Have children share their stories.

Name: ______________________ Date: ______________

ADJECTIVES

Remember

Nouns name people, places, and things.
Adjectives are words that tell about nouns.

Find the word that tells about the noun.
Write it on the line.

1. Did you find a secret attic?

    ______________________ attic

2. Boxes hold many surprises.

    ______________________ surprises

3. You may find old toys.

    ______________________ toys

4. Share them with a new friend.

    ______________________ friend

Extension: Have children name a favorite toy and tell why it is fun. Point out adjectives they used.

Name: ______________________ Date: ______________

WORDS FOR SMELL AND TASTE

Remember

Adjectives tell about people, places, and things.
Some adjectives tell how things smell or taste.

Read the sentences.
Look at the noun that is underlined.
Write the word that tells how it smells or tastes.

1. Rain brings fresh water.

____

2. You can smell clean air.

____

3. It has a new smell.

____

4. Cold water has the best taste.

____

Extension: Have children name adjectives to describe a glass of lemonade on a hot day.

Name: ______________________ Date: ______________

How Things Sound

Remember

Adjectives are words that tell about people, places, or things.
Some adjectives tell how things sound.

noisy birds **buzzing** bee

The last word in the sentence names a thing.
Write the word from the box to tell how it sounds.

chirping	crunchy	buzzing	noisy

1. All the animals were talking in the ______________ woods.

2. Jo stepped on dry ______________ leaves.

3. She saw a ______________ bird.

4. Be careful of the ______________ bees.

Extension: Have children cut out pictures of objects in magazines and use adjectives to describe the pictures.

Name: Date:

ADJECTIVES FOR LOOK AND FEEL

Remember

Adjectives tell how things look.
Adjectives tell how things feel.

Read the sentences.
Find the adjectives that tell how things look or feel.
Circle the adjective in each sentence.

1. Tim has a pretty dog named Fluffy.

2. Fluffy has a white coat.

3. Fluffy has curly hair.

4. Tim uses a stiff brush.

5. Then Fluffy has shiny hair.

Extension: Have children describe a pet. Point out adjectives they use for appearance and feel.

Name: ______________________ Date: ______________

Using Adjectives

Remember

Adjectives are words that tell about a person, place, or thing.
Some adjectives tell how things smell, taste, sound, look, and feel.

Read the foods on the list.
Write an adjective to tell about each food.

1. Milk ______________________
2. Sandwich ______________________
3. Celery ______________________
4. Yogurt ______________________
5. Soup ______________________

Extension: Have children add foods to the menu and describe them.

Name: ____________________ Date: ____________

TELLING ABOUT WEATHER

Remember

Adjectives tell about things.
Some adjectives tell about the weather.

cold **sunny**

Each picture shows the weather.
Write an adjective under each picture.
Choose a word from the box.

snowy	sunny	rainy	cloudy

1. ____________________

2. ____________________

3. ____________________

4. ____________________

Extension: Have children look at pictures for weather in the daily newspaper.

Name: ______________________ Date: ______________

ADJECTIVES FOR WEATHER

Remember

Adjectives tell about things.
Some adjectives tell about the weather.

Read the sentences.
Write each adjective on the line.

1. It was a sunny day.

____

2. The cloudy morning passed.

____

3. We liked the cool air.

____

4. Strong winds blew.

____

Extension: Have children talk about what happens to a boat in stormy weather.

More Adjectives for Weather

Remember

Adjectives describe things.
Some adjectives describe the weather.

Read the sentences. Choose a word from the box to complete each sentence. Write the word on the line.

windy	cool	cloudy	rainy

1. It is fun to fly a kite on a _______________ day.
2. I like to feel the _______________ raindrops.
3. It is a wet and _______________ day.
4. There is not much sun on a

_______________ day.

Extension: Have children use adjectives to describe their favorite kinds of weather.

Name: ______________________ Date: ______________

CHOOSING ADJECTIVES

Remember

Adjectives tell about things.
Some adjectives tell about the weather.

Complete each sentence.
Choose a word from the box.

rainy	hot	cold	snowy

1. I make a  on ______________ days.

2. I wear  on ______________ days.

3. I carry an  in ______________ weather.

4. I go to the  in ______________ weather.

Extension: Have children tell what they do in the weather named in each sentence.

Name: ______________________ Date: ______________

WRITING ABOUT WEATHER

Remember

Adjectives tell about things.
Some adjectives tell about weather.

Look at each picture.
Write an adjective to describe the weather.

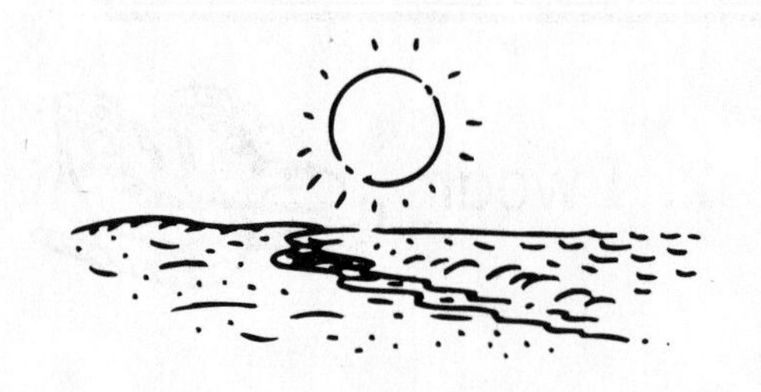

1. ______________________

2. ______________________

3. ______________________

4. ______________________

Extension: Have children describe their favorite kind of weather and tell what they like to do.

Name: ______________________ Date: ______________

Number Words

Remember

Adjectives are words that describe people, places, and things.
Some adjectives are number words.

Read each sentence.
Draw a line under each adjective.

1. Sally has one cat.

2. She likes her white cat.

3. Jimmy has two bears.

4. He plays with the black bears.

5. There are three toys on the bed.

Extension: Have children write a sentence that uses a number word as an adjective.

FINDING NUMBER WORDS

Remember

Adjectives describe people, places, and things.
Some adjectives are number words.

Draw a circle around each number word.

1. Jim has six cars. 

2. Beth has four cars. 

3. Mark has two cars. 

4. Tina has five cars. 

5. Ed has one car. 

Name: ______________________ Date: ______________

HOW MANY?

Remember

Adjectives tell about people, places, and things.
Some adjectives are number words.

Write a number word for each picture.

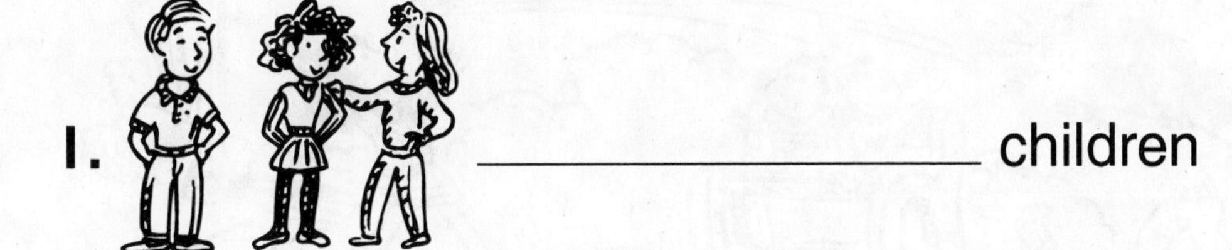

1. ______________ children

2. ______________ cups of water

3. ______________ flowers

4. ______________ girl

Extension: Have children use number words to describe objects in the classroom.

CHOOSING NUMBER WORDS

Remember

You can use number words to describe people.
You can use number words to describe animals.

Look at the picture.
Complete each sentence with a number word.

1. There are ______________ children playing ball.

2. There are ______________ squirrels running.

3. There are ______________ birds flying.

4. There are ______________ babies smiling.

Extension: Have children talk about how many children it takes to play a particular game.

Name: ______________________ Date: ______________

HATS AND CAPS?

Remember

Some adjectives are number words.
Number words can tell about people.

Look at the picture.
Complete each sentence with a number word.

1. I see ____________________ men in hats.

2. I see ____________________ children with caps.

3. I see ____________________ women in big hats.

4. I see ____________________ cap on the sign.

Extension: Have children tell how many people in class are wearing sneakers and how many are wearing something that is red.

Name: ______________________ Date: ______________________

COLOR WORDS ARE ADJECTIVES

Remember

A word that tells about a person, place, or thing is an adjective.
Some adjectives are color words.

Look at each picture.
Choose a color word that tells about each picture.
Write the word on the line.

blue	green	yellow	black

1. ______________________

2. ______________________

3. ______________________

4. ______________________

Extension: Have children name an item they like and write three adjectives to describe it.

Name: ____________________ Date: ____________

Finding Color Words

Remember

Some adjectives are color words.

Read each sentence. Each sentence has two adjectives. Write the adjective that is a color word on the line.

1. Ellen wears big brown boots.

   ____

2. She has a round red bucket.

   ____

3. The shells sit on the long yellow beach.

   ____

4. The beach has smooth white shells.

   ____

Extension: Have children use color words to tell about a collection of their own such as shells, stamps, or toys.

Name: ______________________ Date: ______________

Using Color Words

Remember

An adjective tells about a person, place, or thing.
Some adjectives are color words.

white	purple	green	blue

The sentences tell a story.
Choose a color word from the box.
Write a color word on each line.

1. A big ____________ box came for the family.

2. ____________ presents were inside it.

3. Fred opened a box with ____________ ribbon.

4. Inside was a big ____________ ball.

Extension: Have children use a color word to tell what is inside an orange package.

Name: ______________________ Date: ______________________

FINDING COLOR WORDS

Remember

Some adjectives are color words.
Color words tell how things look.

Read the story.
Circle the color word for each sentence.

1. Lee wore his old blue shoes.

2. He kicked up brown rocky dirt.

3. Lee looked at the beautiful green grapes.

4. He wanted a big red apple.

Extension: Have children tell about a fruit they like. Remind them to use color words.

Name: ______________________ Date: ______________

USING COLOR WORDS

Remember

Some adjectives are color words.
Use color words to tell about things.

The picture shows a market.
Tell what you see.
Use color words as adjectives.

____

____

____

____

Name: ____________ Date: ____________

ADJECTIVES THAT COMPARE

Remember

You can use adjectives to compare things.
Some adjectives end in **er** and **est**.

Find the adjective in each sentence.
Write it on the line.

1. A mouse is small.

____

2. That is a big bear.

____

3. A beetle is smaller than a mouse.

____

4. An elephant is the biggest animal on land.

____

Extension: Have children name two animals and tell which is larger.

COMPARE WITH ER

Remember

Some adjectives compare two things.
Some adjectives that compare end in **er.**

tall taller

Read each sentence.
Circle the adjective that ends in **er.**

1. A turtle walks slower than a cat.

2. A bear is stronger than a mouse.

3. A giraffe is taller than a zebra.

4. A monkey moves faster than a beetle.

5. A cat is smaller than a lion.

Extension: Have children make a comparison between two animals they name.

Name: ______________________ Date: ______________

COMPARE WITH EST

Remember

Some adjectives compare more than two things.
Use **est** to compare more than two things.

Write the adjective that compares more than two things.
Use **est.**

1. Compare ducks, whales, and seals.

   Whales dive the (deep) ______________.

2. Compare a butterfly, a bee, and a duck.

   A duck flies the (fast) ______________.

3. Compare fleas, horses, and spiders.

   Horses are the (long) ______________.

4. Compare a dog, a mouse, and a turtle.

   A turtle is the (slow) ______________.

4

Extension: Have children write a sentence naming the smallest animal they ever saw.

Name: ______________________ Date: ______________

USING ER AND EST

Remember

Adjectives can compare.
Use **er** to compare two things.
Use **est** to compare more than two.

Choose a word from the box to complete each sentence. Write the word on the line.

tallest	louder	coldest	stronger

1. This band plays ______________ than that band.

2. This rope is ______________ than that rope.

3. This hill is the ______________ one in the park.

4. Today is the ______________ day of the year.

Extension: Have children name a riding toy that goes fast, then name one that goes faster, and one that goes the fastest of all.

Name: ______________________ Date: ______________________

DESCRIBING THINGS

Circle each adjective below. Find the things that are compared in the picture. Then write the adjectives on the lines below.

1. This pine tree grows taller than that one. ______________________

2. The beetle is the smallest animal here. ______________________

3. The bird is the fastest animal in the park. ______________________

4. The snail is the slowest animal of all. ______________________

5. This path is longer than that one. ______________________

Extension: Have children describe a park. Have them name things that can be compared.

Name: Date:

WORDS THAT MEAN THE SAME

Remember

All words have meanings.
Sometimes two words mean almost the same thing.

high tall

Look at each word in list A.
A word in list B means almost the same thing.
Draw a line to match the words that mean almost the same thing.

A	B
1. look	small
2. tiny	see
3. smile	grin
4. big	chop
5. cut	large

Extension: Have children use a word from A in a sentence. Then ask them to substitute the matching word from B.

Name: ______________________ Date: ______________

SAME MEANINGS

Remember

Two words can mean almost the same thing.

walk step

You can use many different words when you tell a story.

Find the underlined words in the story. Choose the word in the box that means almost the same. Write the word on the line.

take	cried	big	can

1. Jill saw a large turtle. ______________

2. "Ah," she said. "I will get it." ______________

3. Turtle called out to her. ______________

4. "Let me go and I may help you." ______________

Extension: Have children tell what the turtle can do to help Jill.

Name: ______________________ Date: ______________________

Opposite Meanings

Remember

Some words are opposite in meaning.

Look at the words in list A. A word in list B means the opposite. Draw a line to match the words that mean the opposite.

	A	B
1.	give	glad
2.	sad	fast
3.	slow	take
4.	wet	small
5.	big	dry

Extension: Have children think of a sentence for words in list A. Then have them substitute one antonym for another to change the meaning of each sentence.

Name: ______________________ Date: ______________

SAME AND OPPOSITE

Remember

Two words can have the same meaning.

jog run

Two words can have opposite meanings.

up down

Look at the two underlined words.
Circle S if the words are the same.
Circle O if the words are opposites.

1. Rain fell in the night. day S O
2. The morning was quiet. noisy S O
3. Stacy walked outside. inside S O
4. Drops fell on her cap. hat S O
5. Stacy was happy. glad S O

Extension: Have students substitute the synonym or antonym for the underlined word and reread the sentence.

Name: Date:

More Same and Opposite

Remember

Sometimes words mean the same thing.
Sometimes words have opposite meanings.

Circle the word that means the same as the first word.

1. say smile tell listen

2. cold day warm cool

3. walk step fast wall

Circle the word that is the opposite of the first word.

4. sad cry glad hope

5. high low tall up

Extension: Have children name a word and give its synonym or antonym.

Name: Date:

PRONOUNS

Remember

A **noun** is a word that names a person, place, or thing. girl boy
A **pronoun** is a word that takes the place of a noun. she he

Sentence **a** names a person or thing.
Sentence **b** uses a pronoun.
Circle the pronoun in each sentence **b**.

1. **a.** John has a wish.

   b. He wants a pet.

2. **a.** Sue is thinking.

   b. Can she buy a mouse?

3. **a.** Amy wants a pet, too.

   b. She wants a guinea pig.

4. **a.** Tim has a dog.

   b. He takes good care of the dog.

Extension: Have children name a person and then name the pronoun for that person.

Name: ______________________ Date: ______________

USING HE, SHE, IT

Remember

He is a pronoun that names a boy or a man.
She is a pronoun that names a girl or a woman.
It is a pronoun that names a thing.

Look at the underlined noun.
Write the correct pronoun on the line.

1. Jonah has two guinea pigs.

   ______________ likes guinea pigs.

2. That guinea pig will be a good pet.

   ______________ is friendly.

3. Lori is busy.

   ______________ is cutting a carrot.

4. The guinea pig eats a carrot.

   The guinea pig likes ______________.

Extension: Have children write a sentence about a guinea pig, beginning, "It eats. . . ."

Name: ______________________ Date: ______________________

USING THEY

Remember

A pronoun takes the place of a noun.
Use **he**, **she**, **it** for one. One guinea pig: **it**
Use **they** for more than one. Two guinea pigs: **they**

Read the pair of sentences.
Write the correct pronoun on the line.

1. What can guinea pigs do?

________________ can play.

2. Do guinea pigs wear funny hats?

________________ do not need hats.

3. What color are the hats?

________________ come in many colors.

4. Put out both your hands.

________________ can hold a guinea pig.

Extension: Have children write a question and an answer about guinea pigs, using the word *they* in the answer.

Name: ______________________ Date: ______________

USING PRONOUNS

Remember

A pronoun takes the place of a noun.
Use **he, she, it** for one.
Use **they** for more than one.

Read the sentences.
The nouns are underlined.
Circle the pronouns that can take their place.

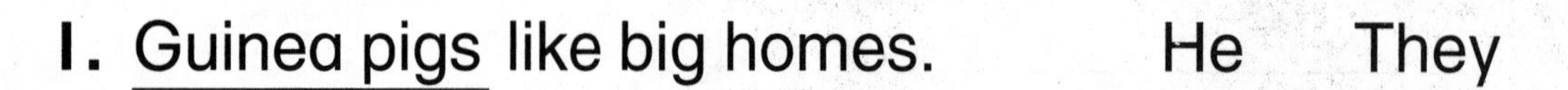

1. Guinea pigs like big homes. He They

2. Sara has a cage. It She

3. The cage is a good home. It They

4. Sunflower seeds are in the cage. They She

5. Tim will feed the pets. It He

Extension: Have children write a sentence about guinea pigs that includes a pronoun.

Name: ______________________ Date: ______________

USING HE, SHE, IT

Remember

A pronoun takes the place of a noun.
Use **he, she, it** to tell about one.
Use **they** to tell about more than one.

Write each sentence again. Use a pronoun in place of each underlined noun.

1. Bill keeps his pet in a cage.

____

2. The pet is a green lizard.

____

3. Sally raises tadpoles in a large bowl.

____

4. The tadpoles will grow into frogs.

____

Extension: Have childen name a pet they would like to have, and write a sentence about it.

Using I and Me

Remember

Use **I** in the naming part of a sentence.
Use **me** in the action part of a sentence.

Read the sentence.
Write **I** or **me** on the line.

1. Who read the letter?

   __________ read the letter.

2. Who wrote the letter to you?

   Mike wrote the letter to __________ .

3. What did Mike say?

   He asked __________ to come to his house.

4. When will you go?

   __________ will go today.

 Extension: Have children write a sentence to answer Mike's invitation.

Name: ______________________ Date: ______________

USING I

Remember

The word **I** is a pronoun.
Use **I** in the naming part of a sentence.

Read each sentence.
Write the pronoun **I** on the line.

1. ____________ can write very well.

2. You and ____________ can write invitations.

3. My brother and ____________ will give a party.

4. You and ____________ will have fun.

5. ____________ like parties.

Extension: Have children write a sentence that begins *You and I.*

Name: ______________________ Date: ______________________

Using Me

Remember

The word **me** is a pronoun.
Use **me** in the action part of a sentence.

Read the sentence.
Write the pronoun **me** on the line.

1. Gina brings mail to ______________ .

2. Every day she gives ______________ letters.

3. She talks to ______________ at my house.

4. She tells ______________ about her job.

5. She helps ______________ with my work.

Extension: Have children write a sentence about someone they meet every day. Have them use the word *me* in the sentence.

Name: ______________________ Date: ______________

Using I and Me

Remember

Use **I** in the naming part of a sentence.
Use **me** in the action part of a sentence.

Write the correct pronoun.
Use **I** or **me.**

1. ______________ like to walk in the rain.

2. The rain gets ______________ all wet.

3. ______________ splash in the puddles.

4. Water makes ______________ feel good.

5. ______________ wish it would rain today.

Extension: Have children write a journal entry, telling how they feel about rainy weather.

Name: ______________________ Date: __________

USING I AND ME IN A STORY

Tell about an adventure you had on a rainy day.
Use **I** and **me** in your story.

Extension: Have childen illustrate their stories and share them with their classmates.